*. . . The Boy Behind the Door . . .*
David is now 24 and
works in a restaurant in Paris.

Evangéline de Schonen is a
psychotherapist at a clinic in Paris.

DAVID BISSON and
EVANGÉLINE DE SCHONEN

# ... *The Boy* ...
# *Behind the Door*

*Translated from the French by David Watson*

Mandarin

*For Tony*

. . .

**A Mandarin Paperback**
THE BOY BEHIND THE DOOR

First published as *L'enfant derrière la porte* in 1993
by Editions Grasset & Fasquelle

First published in Great Britain 1994
by Mandarin Paperbacks
an imprint of Reed Consumer Books Ltd
Michelin House, 81 Fulham Road, London SW3 6RB
and Auckland, Melbourne, Singapore and Toronto

Copyright © Editions Grasset & Fasquelle 1993
Translation copyright © 1994 by David Watson

A CIP catalogue record for this title
is available from the British Library
ISBN 0 7493 1706 X

Phototypeset by Intype, London
Printed and bound in Great Britain
by Cox & Wyman Ltd, Reading, Berks

# PREFACE

I have kept the drawing which David did for me on the day of our first meeting. He had portrayed himself in the form of a piece of excrement.

His long ordeal had damaged the very things every child needs to develop to take their place in life: self-esteem and self-respect.

Did this account for his retarded growth? David was small for his age, and in the two years following the end of his captivity he had trouble growing. Medical examinations failed to uncover the exact cause of this blockage.

David has done a lot of work on the hate which he talks about in this book. In effect, he has managed to expel it in the way one might dig out a splinter which is causing pain. He has examined it, has tried to understand, to tie together the broken threads of his story, to re-establish the truths he needs to build himself as a human being.

Once he had exorcised his hate and rediscovered

compassion, a taste for tenderness, 'forgiveness without realising it' (as he puts it), images from his childhood, dreams of warmth and family security, David began to catch up on his lost growth – an astonishing testimony to the inner resources of the human being.

Courage was something David never lacked. He has fought long and hard that his story should not be told or written without his consent. He needed courage to write this account with Evangéline de Schonen, to reawaken fading memories, like a scalpel reopening fresh scar tissue. It demonstrated a supreme effort on David's part to rid himself of the tragic curse which had blighted his destiny and to prevent the wound from healing over before he had been able to defuse the explosive emotional charge within.

Over the course of our meetings I have learned a lot from David about traumatic experiences like his and the way in which they become revised by the work of memory. This made the writing of a book today worthwhile, a work whose surrealistic truth guides us to the limits of the human condition, showing us the strange forms of parent/child relationships and the extent to which a child's desire to live and understand can bring him salvation.

'Gradually we learned how to talk to each other without an intermediary . . . It was a real learning process . . . I was learning not to see them in a bad light . . . Let the hate go, disappear . . . I needed a family, roots . . . Attempt to create a real family . . . One or two years were enough to placate and relieve my hatred . . . I had found forgiveness, without realising it.'

Has David ever been allowed to be a child? And how has he managed to realise Goethe's idea that one can never become an adult without understanding one's parents and forgiving them?

It is true that, from our very first meetings when David had just escaped from his prison, he displayed a surprisingly sharp and mobile intelligence. He used it to question himself on all the stages of his existence, including his decision to choose freedom.

The little boy who stood before me, solid on his own two feet, searched for, discovered then communicated his story in a language which was elaborate and precise. A paper-thin voice. Mustn't make a noise. Mustn't draw attention to his presence. Yet he was full of humour and very shrewd, eager to speak, quick to make associations of thoughts and images, always able to grasp the meaning in them.

Locked away in his cupboard, deprived of what he needed, particularly the toys which all children need to grow up, David must have listened a lot and played with the words and images he was able to glean and with the stories he created in his head . . .

Tony Lainé

I was stricken with fear. When I went into the courtroom I had the feeling that I had made a huge mistake, that I was the one who was guilty. I closed my eyes and wished with all my might that it would all be over as quickly as possible.

I was in a nightmare. I was accompanied by a counsellor. In front of us were the magistrate and three other people. I also spotted two lawyers and a witness. But I didn't dare look any further.

I had merely glanced behind me on the way in to see if my parents were there. There was no one.

I felt hemmed in, caught in a trap. I can't explain it. I no longer knew why I was there. All my thoughts were confused. I stared at the ground and the magistrate asked me questions I didn't understand. I said whatever came into my head and looked at the hangings on the wall.

At one point I heard someone say that a lady in the jury had broken down.

I think that was the worst moment of my life.

It was my mother's trial. In closed session.

But the trial took place without me, as if I was never there. The inquiry was just a huge blur, I went through it like a ghost.

My brother had asked me to say nothing about what had happened. He was sad, mainly for his father, I think. For his sake, everything I stated at the tribunal was the opposite of what I thought. If he hadn't been there I would never have lied to the judges. I even think I would have said: 'Convict her!'

She could have gone to prison for twenty years, maybe more . . . I don't know. My step-father would have got off lightly, I think.

But anyway, I didn't defend myself, I gave way, I was all alone with my story which I didn't even tell . . .

# THE BOY BEHIND THE DOOR

It was my turn to help my brother. I don't regret it. He helped me a lot when I was locked up. I owed him a debt.

Above all, what was so difficult was having to go back over the course of those years of madness. Later, I wrote to the Minister of Justice. They were let out shortly afterwards. But that's another story.

I was born on 29 May 1970 at Angers.

At the time, my mother was working on the railways as a stewardess or cleaner, I'm not sure which, on the sleeping-cars. On the Paris-Nantes line. During one of these journeys she got off to give birth to me. That's how I came to be born in Angers.

She didn't stop working when she was expecting. She never said a word about it. Even then she was hiding me away. In a way, you could say that I had a bit of a rough landing.

She wanted to leave me at the maternity hospital, but they wouldn't let her. She must surely have been in a very difficult situation to consider doing that. She was all alone, without any support, without a man by her side. I was a burden to her.

She went straight back to work and left me with a nurse from the very first months of my life.

So there was no father for me at my birth.

When I try to get back to my earliest memories, the image that comes immediately to mind is that of the sea.

My very first thoughts are linked with an old woman at the seaside. I can't remember which sea it was. The coast of Normandy? The Atlantic?

I only have scraps of images, fragmentary scenes, like old photos turning up again, or even short pieces of film . . .

I can't remember the foster mother's name. I think she was quite old. She lived in an old apartment all in wood; the building was slightly red, like an English house. Hers looked out onto a beach with huts. I spent a lot of time on that beach, playing and eating cakes. There were also landing stages and a harbour for pleasure boats where we often went for walks.

# THE BOY BEHIND THE DOOR

She looked after me well and I think she loved me very much. All that remains is the sweetness of those memories . . .

One day we went on a train journey; we were going to the countryside. It was very green, very beautiful. There was a huge garden, more like a park, in fact. We played lots of football and hide-and-seek. It was really good.

My life with this foster mother is one of my oldest and best memories. I don't know how long I spent with her. I don't know how old I was, I was very small. But of all the things I can remember, that house is where I would have liked to stay.

After that lady I had other foster mothers. I may not remember them so much, but they were part of my life and certainly important.

I went to a very nice foster mother in the suburbs of Paris. I liked it there. Every morning I was allowed a glass of milk. It was a good tonic. She had a caravan in her garden where I had a lot of fun. I must have stayed with her a fair while. But oddly enough I have very few clear memories of that time, few images of it.

That's where my mother came to fetch me.

She arrived one day at the home of this foster mother with the caravan in her garden, where I was happy. She wanted to take me home with her. She was living with a man, whom I took to be my father, and a baby, who was my brother.

I struggled when she tried to take me away. I threw a real tantrum. I refused point blank to go with her.

I didn't want to go back with her. It's true. I didn't know her at all. I had no experience of her, no memory. She was a stranger to me. She had left me at birth. My feelings for her were so few, so poor – in fact, I had almost none at all.

It must have been very hard for her.

I had trouble accepting that she was my

mother. I didn't trust her. In fact I felt total mistrust towards her from the very start.

I refused to kiss her or talk to her. I was already stubborn in matters of the heart. She must have been very disappointed in me. Perhaps that's what sent her mad.

It was a building with a pointed roof, in Neuilly-sur-Marne. We lived on the third floor in a three-room apartment: an entrance hall, a living room and a bedroom, a small kitchen and a bathroom.

There were black and white tiles on the floor and all the shutters were painted claret.

I have very clear memories of the parts of this apartment, where I spent the most time.

As you came in, on the left against the wall, there was a very beautiful, heavy, old oakwood dresser. On the right, a cupboard and, next to it, the door to the bathroom. Facing the front door was the door to the main room. Immediately on the right there was a sort of recess, a kitchen space, which didn't have a door and opened directly onto the living room. I remember a round glass table in that kitchen where we sometimes ate.

# THE BOY BEHIND THE DOOR

In the main room the window was on the right-hand wall. There was a large beige sofa where I don't think I ever sat, an armchair, an oak-wood table and a television. The door to the bedroom was opposite the window in the left-hand wall.

My mother's bed was on the right, next to a wardrobe in white wood with brown doors, and the one my brother and I slept in, in the beginning, was at the end of the room, against the left-hand wall, near the window.

There was only one bedroom. My mother, my stepfather, my brother and I, later my brother on his own, all slept together.

In the beginning, my brother was just a baby and I must have been about two. There were two bunk-beds for us, but I suppose he must have slept in a cradle when he was little.

In the first year my mother had given up work to look after her 'children'; or rather, her new baby. Already, the only attention I got was anger and beatings.

My stepfather, on the other hand, played with us. Just like a normal father! I remember, he was very big and he had a large moustache.

Then my mother went back to work on the

sleeping-cars. I think we sometimes went with my stepfather to meet her at the station. My brother and I went back to a childminder. The days passed quietly.

I always wanted to climb into my brother's pushchair. The childminder said I was too big, that I was a big boy and as I was the eldest I should walk! Oh well!

My brother didn't like going to the child-minder's. He preferred to stay at home. I, on the other hand, did like it. It was quite normal for me and it was more peaceful. I felt com-pletely fine there.

After her we were with another childminder, where we sometimes stayed the night.

I can now say that I had a feeling, a sort of premonition, that there was something going wrong between my mother and me. The situation at home was becoming more and more difficult. The punishments started very quickly. They were brutal. The beatings were usually to do with food. I was a poor eater, and very slow.

It happened at meal-times. We would be seated at the table. At that time I still had a plate and a knife and fork like everybody else. She would give me a few minutes to clear my plate. Not a moment more. I took a long time to finish. She wouldn't stand for it. Sometimes I couldn't even swallow what she gave me.

For example, there was a tripe dish which we often had, which I flatly refused and which she forced me to swallow. It made me sick every time. Then she would get into such a fury that she might do anything to me.

She made me kneel for hours on a metal bar with my nose against the wall. Or else she locked me in the bathroom for days on end. Or else, at night, I was deprived of my bed and made to sleep on the floor in the entrance hall. That's apart from the smacks and blows she gave me for no apparent reason.

As well as that, the top bunk-bed had been removed. There was only one bed left in the room, my brother's. From then on I slept either in the hall or in the bathroom. Sometimes I could use a foam mattress in the hall or a rug which I could wrap myself up in. But that didn't stop me getting very cold from the draught under the front door.

She terrorised me. I didn't dare make a

single movement when she was there. I stayed in the position she had put me in when she punished me.

There was also my silence. Since I had come back to live with them I hadn't spoken to her. Not at all. I couldn't say a word to her. It was something stronger than me. I would look at her. That's all. I was on my guard all the time. She must have resented me for that as well.

Thinking back on it, she would lose her temper with me for almost anything.

One day I had trouble saying the word 'yoghurt'. She made me say it all day until I managed to pronounce it properly. With a few slaps as a reward.

Or else, another time, she made me sort a pile of shoes into pairs. Of course, I got it wrong. So I earned a good hiding.

One day, I don't know why, I threw a stone at my brother and split his skull. He had to go to hospital. And I spent several days on my knees with my nose against the wall.

At that time we were still going to a child-minder. She had children of her own, including a girl who knew us well since we slept at her house every now and again. One evening, I told her what happened at home. How my mother treated me, the punishments, beatings, etc.

Of course, my mother learned about what I had said from the childminder. I wasn't allowed to have a childminder ever again.

It was one evening or morning, I forget which. I was kneeling in the hall, as a punishment, I expect. My mother was moving about the house. I had a terrible sense of foreboding. I was sure that something serious was about to happen. I looked at the bathroom door. 'Let her take me to the childminder, let me get out of here . . .' I was absolutely petrified. I could hardly breathe. I waited.

Then she grabbed hold of me. She put me in the bathroom and locked the door. I was locked up, alone, without a light. For how long? I was four and a half.

From that moment on I never left the bathroom. My hands and feet tied, I was entirely in my mother's power.

No one knows my mother better than I. Not my stepfather. Not my brother.

I'm the one who got closest to her, who knew her from the inside, in all her forms.

Sometimes I wonder whether I dreamt it. Whether it was one enormous nightmare . . .?

But I know very well that it wasn't . . .

From the moment that I stopped going to the childminder, I spent almost the whole time tied to the pipe in the bathroom between the sink, the toilet and the bath.

As in the rest of the apartment the floor was covered in black and white tiles, and was cold; I remember the sky-blue ceramic walls.

There was a window in this bathroom, through which, when the shutters were open, which they rarely were, I could see the sky and the awnings of the building opposite.

Mostly I was tied, with my head turned to the wall, by a chain around my waist, attached to a dog's lead or another chain which was wrapped around the pipe in the lower part of the wall.

The chain cut into my waist whenever I moved or tried to stretch out. I've still got some weird scars from it.

She locked me in and bound me there by sealing all the openings around me: the shutters were padlocked and, as the door didn't have a lock, she devised a system with nails and string to keep it shut from the outside.

Days followed nights, all exactly the same, punctuated only by bouts of madness.

In the evening, after they had eaten dinner, she would bring me some food which she would place on the edge of the bath. It was either a pan or a bowl, without a knife or fork, only a spoon. It had their left-overs, a colourless mishmash which often tasted disgusting.

In the morning I was allowed a bowl of

white coffee with some bread in it, or some soup, which she left me before going to work.

During the day I had oranges or apples. Occasionally a little cheese. Sometimes nothing at all. When they went out they shut off the water. If I was thirsty I drank what was left in the taps. When that ran out I took water from the toilet; by pulling on my chain I just about managed it.

When they went away for the weekend I knew, because she would untie me and leave me a little more food. I stayed locked up in the bathroom.

One time when they went away like that I remember I started banging on the door and shouting at the top of my voice: 'I'm locked in the bathroom . . . the shutters and the door are locked . . .' Then I listened for someone coming. Nothing. No reaction. I tried this several times. I felt like I was hammering away in a vacuum. I gave up. I don't know if anyone heard but in any case no one came. I went back to the silence. Abandoned. A weekend is a long time. I got by with whatever she had left me to eat.

# THE BOY BEHIND THE DOOR

Sometimes they had friends round and I was allowed to come out of the bathroom. There were lots of people and everything went well. It was a chance to make some noise. I had a good pair of lungs and my mother or my stepfather would say: 'Be quiet, don't make so much noise.' Their friends didn't particularly notice me. I played with my brother. These were interludes.

My brother went to school and came home in the evening with my mother or my stepfather. He was kept at home after school. I didn't have much contact with him at that time.

There was also a little dog called Jessy. She was the only one who didn't harm me. I had some nice times with her, furtively, in secret, but these were very rare. She was a little dachshund, and was mainly my stepfather's dog. She used to come and have a pee in the bathroom every now and again. Sometimes I managed to stroke her.

Later she would stay with me in the bedroom, lying on the bed. We became friends. I had a lot of affection for her. They were my only ties of friendship. She came with me to the home after my escape.

I followed the rhythm of their lives without living it. I knew all their movements. I got my bearings from the sounds they made in the apartment. I heard everything.

They came in to wash in rotation. My mother would have a bath; my stepfather as well. I avoided looking at them. Maybe sometimes it intrigued me, interested me even. But for the most part I stayed still, my head turned to the wall, waiting for them to leave the bathroom. So long as they left me alone and forgot I was there I didn't care that they walked around stark naked under my very nose. I was still little at that time, five or six years old, perhaps?

However, I have a very bad memory of them being in the bathroom one time. I was probably older then and things weren't quite so straightforward in my head. They must have been still in love at that time. She came in to wash her hair, I remember it well. He came into the bathroom, and then they were all over each other, as if I didn't even exist, as if I was just an animal that didn't understand anything. I can't explain, but I felt really bad.

She untied me in order to wash me. She always washed me in cold water. No hot water for me. Even later, in Brétigny, when I was grown up, I could never wash by myself.

I wore a minimal amount of clothes. Underpants, a vest, sometimes some trousers, and when it was really cold a pullover. That's all. She changed me quite often.

My brother was the lucky one. He had a hot bath every day. With bubble-bath. He soaked in the bath for hours, with his toys – at least it seemed like ages to me!

I was next to the bath, tied to my pipe and he lorded it like a prince in his bubble-bath, quite indifferent, at least it seemed that way. He didn't speak to me. I spoke even less. My mother was never far away. We were afraid of reprisals later.

In the evening I heard them watching television until quite late. My brother was in bed.

# THE BOY BEHIND THE DOOR

Often my stepfather went to bed before my mother.

Then night came.

Then the terror began.

It was mainly at night that she tormented me, that she put me through the mill. She would have real bouts of madness. She would close all the doors – of her bedroom, of the living room and of the bathroom. She shut herself in with me. Then she would improvise as she went along, as her fury increased.

It often involved water. Or fire.

I was afraid that I would die, that I would drown in the bath.

She would fill the bath with cold water, tie my hands, take me by the feet, lower me head first into the water and hold me there for ages. I must have been good at holding my breath . . .

Other times she would hang me by the feet from the handle of the toilet, with my head in the bowl, and flush it.

Her anger would increase tenfold when I held on to the pipe with all my might so that she couldn't take me.

I think I had a lot of strength to resist her then.

I had long hair. She would burn it with her lighter. She would set it on fire, then extinguish it. It was as if it was a game for her. Or else she would pour some methylated spirit on the floor next to me and set light to that.

Once, she sprayed all my clothes with bleach which burned my eyes.

Often, after these nights of torture, she would tie my hands behind my back with a very tight piece of string just before she left for work. And I would stay tied up like that until my stepfather came home and untied me. The marks the string made were so deep they burned me.

On the nights she left me alone, I slept lying on the ground or, when the chain was too tight, leaning against the side of the bath.

One day, she burned my hands. I must have been four or five years old. I had already been locked up for a long time. At least in my mind it seemed a long time.

# THE BOY BEHIND THE DOOR

I was underneath the sink, as usual. She gave me an apple and said: 'Eat that up quickly, you'd better make sure you've finished it before I get back.'

I munched the apple, quietly. I always had trouble swallowing.

I heard her come back and I hadn't finished. I put what was left in my mouth and tried to swallow it as quickly as I could. I choked on it. So she came in in a real temper. She ran some boiling water into the bidet. She grabbed hold of me, put a towel over my head to stifle the screams, jammed me between her legs and plunged my hands into the water.

I felt a tingling, like an electric shock at the ends of my fingers. I must have struggled, but she was obviously too strong for me.

'Let it be over with quickly . . .' At the beginning I managed to withdraw my left hand; my right hand stayed in. She held them under the water. When she let go, my hands were bright red.

That evening, I don't know what she told my stepfather. I had third degree burns on my hands. They dressed them with gauze bandages, it was hell! My skin was raw. But I didn't cry out when she was attending to me, she frightened me too much.

A lot later, they took me to the hospital for a skin-graft. Some skin had formed between my fingers, like I had webbed hands. But it was too complicated to graft on some new skin. They would have had to take some skin from my back. I was probably too young.

I have good memories of the trip to the hospital. I walked around the corridors. I had some nice pyjamas, very soft. The nurses made a fuss over me. They said I was a bonny lad. No one knew anything about my other life.

Once, I had a visit from a bearded man, a counsellor perhaps, I don't know. He was nice. We talked about cars and other things. Just everyday things. I was in a good mood, in good health, happy to be there. He had no idea, that man in front of me, about what went on at home.

I was far too afraid that no one would believe me. I was ashamed as well, for sure. Perhaps the adults would have stuck together. So I kept quiet.

Something strange happened on that occasion. We were talking, I filled the sink with water and thrust my hand towel into it. He looked at me, surprised. He must have thought I'd suddenly gone mad. Now that I talk about it I can relate this action to my burnt hands. They had been burned by boiling water and my screams were stifled by a towel. I was trying to say something to this bearded man.

Then, one day, my stepfather came to fetch me and I went back to the bathroom and the silence.

'You never speak,' he said reproachfully. That was true, I said nothing. But what could I talk to them about?

My hands have become a psychological handicap for me. Even though I have begun to come to terms with what I have long considered to be an infirmity.

Luckily, when I was little, the pain was less serious.

Later, at school, it caused me a lot of problems. This, on top of the fact that I was older than the other children, which was difficult enough in itself! We played 'round the mulberry bush', but I could see that no one was exactly fighting to get next to me. They avoided me. And when they didn't have any choice they gave me their hand but held me by the wrist. That got to me. It made me feel even more different from them. I don't know if the teacher noticed. But I was very unhappy.

One day, I was walking with people from my brother's school. A teacher reprimanded me. I never took my hands out of my coat pocket. We were in a café. The teacher said loudly: 'David, take your hands out of your pockets.' I was very upset: I felt like the whole café was looking at me. However, he was right, that teacher. I took them out very slowly and nothing happened.

Now that I am an adult it doesn't bother me. I'm used to it. I don't think about it any more, except at certain moments, on public transport, for example. I can still sense people staring but deep down I'm used to it.

But if it were possible one day, I would still like to try to have a skin graft on both hands. Perhaps later in life . . .

Inside my bathroom I don't think I imagined anything. I mean that I did form images in my head from what I heard, what I saw and my memories of the childminders. That's all. I had no conception of the world outside and its complications. My images were born from sounds, from changes of light. For example, when it was sunny and if the window and the shutters were open, I could see the reflection of the blue sky in the bathroom mirror. I saw the awnings and the balconies of the building opposite. It made me think about the old lady by the sea and the boats. I immediately think about the sea whenever there is a bit of blue in the sky.

Even without imagination my thoughts

unfurled. These thoughts, these dreams, helped me to survive. I've lost some of these thoughts since I got out. There are so many things to do in life. I have less time to think.

My life was limited to the wall, the bathroom pipe, my chain, whether or not my mother was there . . . But I heard a lot, all the time, all the sounds, outside: conversations from downstairs in the building, those of my family in the apartment. Children shouting in the playground, just down below. I played with them, I heard them going back to school. I heard cars drive past, I saw shadows on the shutters. All that kept me alive. It was a little as if I was joining in the lives of other people, outside.

When my brother went back to school, he sometimes brought friends home. I heard them playing in the bedroom or the living room.

Later, when I had been to my grandmother's house, I found comfort in my images of my life with her: they, at least, really existed!

Through this bathroom door, I basically knew everything that went on. Hearing was surviving. These words remain.

I don't remember being seriously ill. I must have had an iron constitution.

One day, she made me swallow some orange peel and I had such a stomach ache! I had hidden the orange peel behind the toilet to play with it and turn it into some little cars on the side of the bath. My mother caught me red-handed. I was forced to swallow my toys.

I suffered from terrible migraines: one of my front teeth was broken when it was hit by the shower head. I can't remember the reason why she hit me. But afterwards I had very bad headaches all the time. Then, one day, the headache disappeared of its own accord.

Now, I have good resistance, I rarely fall ill, and I always take care of it myself; it soon gets better. I'm used to it, I've had lots of practice . . .

Physical pain is quickly forgotten. She always tried to hurt me, hurt me badly, she was a real tormentor. But my real pain is mental.

Some of my memories are hard to bear: Christmas, for example. I heard them through the door. They were celebrating. My brother was being given presents, lots of presents. I wasn't allowed anything, except to listen to them from the bathroom. My brother was their beloved child, I was just an animal. But even an animal would be treated better.

I had a strong feeling of injustice compared to my brother. Why me? Me, alone, in this situation?

This rage which she visited on me . . . I was like a punchbag to her.

Thinking back now, our relationship had something animalistic about it. It was a story of wild beasts. A language of wild beasts. We never talked. If she spoke to me, I didn't reply.

At the start of every day I never knew what was waiting for me. Sometimes she might arrive home early from work. She would be there from early afternoon. She would be alone with me. Like at night-time . . . Things might happen then, in exactly the same way.

My legs would shake as soon as I heard her voice or sensed her presence in the apartment. In the end, I was afraid all the time. When she wasn't there, I rested. When she came back, I was in a state of tension. Resisting took up all my energy.

She often had a bamboo stick in her hand, which would appear out of nowhere. She would come towards me, telling me to be quiet: 'I don't want to hear a sound, otherwise I carry on.' And she would beat the living daylights out of me.

Once, I had hidden some apple pips behind the toilet. Probably so I could play with them later. When she spotted them she went into such a rage that she took off her stiletto shoe, the right foot, I remember, and split my head open. She went at me so relentlessly and with such violence that I bled like a pig. I think she was very scared that day.

When I heard her arrive I would take hold of

the bathroom pipe and hang on with all my strength. She found it hard to make me let go. That made her more angry. Then she would grip me tightly round the neck, strangling me. I saw white dots before my eyes. At times like this she would use blackmail: 'I won't do anything to you if you let go of the pipe.'

Another place I could hang on to was the oak dresser in the hall. Sometimes she would untie me. I sometimes ended up in the hallway, almost underneath the dresser. I can remember a large kitchen knife next to my face. I gritted my teeth. I was hanging on to the dresser, scared out of my wits. I felt that she might kill me, that if I opened my mouth something terrible would happen.

I can't say now what it was that made her take out her kitchen knife.

These humiliations and tortures which were part of everyday life were to do with food. She made me swallow my vomit when I had been sick in disgust at the stinking food which she had forced me to eat.

Sometimes I dreamed of making her pay. I

said to myself: 'If I get out of here I'll lynch her.'

I don't know why she did all these things to me. But in all her fits of anger, I, a little boy, could see by her face that she was mad.

I do remember one interlude in all this horror. A good interlude. It seems so far away now. I don't know exactly what happened that day; but I remember this small detail: that day I went out with my mother. I was quite small and I had already been locked up for a long time.

My stepfather was having some of his friends round and she probably didn't want to see them, or at least didn't want to be at home.

She didn't know where to put me. We went down into the basement. We did a tour around it. She said that she might perhaps leave me in the cellar. I simply refused – possibly quite firmly. Anyway, she took me with her. We walked around for the whole day.

At one point she even asked me if I wanted

to go and see someone, some man, I think. I didn't understand. Maybe it was a friend of hers. I refused. We went for a drink in a bar. Then we went for a walk again. I was so surprised that she was walking with me . . .! And I talked. I didn't stop talking. I remember: it was evening, just before we went home. I talked about everything I saw: planes in the sky, cars . . . I told stories. I was relaxed. No longer on my guard. I made her laugh. She really did laugh.

Then night fell. We went home. I went back to the bathroom. She brought me some grated carrots in a salad bowl; there was lots; I took my time. I heard what she said to my stepfather, who had gone to bed. My brother was already asleep. The guests had gone. And I took too long to eat my carrots. So it all started again, just like before; the blows rained down, her sudden anger . . .

It was just the space of one day. A state of grace . . .? I never knew what had really happened that day.

At the age of nine I moved into the family bedroom. I say nine now, but at the time I had no idea how old I was.

I was tied to their bed, just next to the wardrobe and the bedside table. I don't know why she decided to move me. Maybe I was too big to stay in the bathroom? Anyway, it was after the two months I spent with my grandmother.

I often lay under the bed. Or sometimes on top of it, underneath a duvet. No one saw me. I was always tied by a chain. In one way, I was more comfortable than in the bathroom. Jessy the little dog kept me company. She slept on the bed all day.

My mother left me a pot, but told me not to use it when she wasn't there. Which wasn't easy! I was terrified of disobeying her, but at the same time, I needed to use it once or twice during the day. This caused the fits of anger I knew so well when she got home in the evening.

Through the bedroom window I could see the branches of a large tree, an oak, I think. A building just behind it, with garages underneath. I could constantly hear children shouting and playing down below.

I lived my life in this room.

During the day, I had peace and quiet. They went to work, and my brother to school.

On the occasions they had friends round they stuck me under the bed.

Some nights she untied me and I could go and sleep in the hallway.

But other evenings, after an angry scene, she would bind my hands behind my back, quite tight, make me kneel at the foot of their bed, yank my head back and say, 'Don't move an inch!' Naturally I didn't dare make a movement, for fear of being beaten. Even when they were asleep I didn't move. My head would drop with tiredness, I would wake up with a start. Then doze off again. I spent many nights like this, watching them sleep.

Sometimes, she kept me tied up under the bed. My presence didn't bother them a bit. I heard them making love above my head. At times like that I was nothing. I simply didn't exist. Crossed out. Swept away. A piece of shit . . .

I think that they were among the hardest and most painful moments to get through.

During one of those days, when I was bored to death, I explored whatever was to hand. In particular, the bedside table.

I found a book – it was yellow and black, I seem to recall. As I was looking at the written pages – I didn't understand a word, of course – a photo fell out. It was my mother with a dark-haired man who wasn't my stepfather. But I could immediately see how much he resembled me. He held my mother round the neck.

Who was this man? I was disturbed, in a state of shock, but unable to ask myself any real questions, since my stepfather was father to me. I put the photo back and returned the book to the beside table.

A vague memory resurfaced, of a time when I wasn't yet locked up and I was watching television, I heard my mother say, 'Look, there's Daddy singing!' I didn't pay any attention. My stepfather was my daddy.

I completely forgot about this, until the day I learned that I wasn't my stepfather's son.

The man who lived with my mother should have been my father. He was tall and had an important-looking moustache. I think he was a handsome man. But he was probably a weak character. Lacking in moral fibre, you might say.

At the start of their life together they must have been in love. He wouldn't do anything to displease my mother. Stay out of any problem. So he let her do as she pleased.

When I was very small he did play with me and my brother. He must have wanted to have a normal life.

From the moment when she locked me in the bathroom everything was ruined, and he let himself get stuck in a vicious circle. And as she was violent, and she did what she did mainly when he wasn't there or asleep . . .

It can't have been very comfortable for him either. He did what he could. Maybe he was also terrorised by his wife . . .?

For example, my mother worked some Sundays. Where? I don't know. In a restaurant? On the till at a supermarket? Whatever, some job she had to go to on a Sunday. On those days, my stepfather untied me and let me out. I ate at the table with him and my brother. With a plate and a knife and fork! I watched television with them and played with my brother.

When the time came for my mother to return home he put me back in the bathroom to avoid any reprisals.

He said very little to me. I was the same, I hardly said a word to him. We had a silent relationship.

One time he even tried to convince my mother to send me to school. I heard him make the suggestion. It was after I returned from grandmother's, so I was nine. But his efforts came to nothing. He didn't succeed.

He was defeated, or whatever. I didn't go to school.

Deep down, I think he wanted peace and quiet, for her to leave him alone. They each had their own child. He had my brother and he left me for my mother to sort out. He wanted to save his skin, and his son's.

He had a good job, in commerce, I think.

He sometimes had a bit on the side. I could tell from the tone of their conversations. They went at it hammer and tongs! And also from seeing my mother sniffing his suits, finding traces of perfume, hairs, searching his pockets, his papers . . . I watched her at it from the bathroom, meticulously. It was amazing . . .!

Some days their relationship was far from stable.

It wasn't until later, after my escape, that I was able to have a normal relationship with him. I would go to see him at the tribunal, before the trial. The visits didn't last long, but we managed to talk freely. I got on quite well with him. I saw him separately from my mother. In fact, they had broken up when they went to prison.

After he got out I went to see him several times at his place. In the Vendôme. He had moved in with another woman. My brother lived with him. Maybe I was expecting something from him. Some sign of him being a father . . . I definitely communicated with him better than with my mother. He tried to find out what had become of me. I don't know what he's doing now. We haven't spoken for a long time.

Perhaps I can count on him now?

As far as I'm concerned, anything is possible . . .


I remember my stepfather's family. It was a chance to get out in the open air!

It was summer. I was about six years old.

They hadn't found anyone to look after me during the holidays. So they had to take me with them to my stepfather's family. First of all they rented a house in the Vaucluse with one of his sisters. He had lots. He was part of a very big family.

We went walking in the mountains. I was afraid of falling over the edge. Afraid that my mother would push me over, to tell the truth.

I slept with them in the tent. My brother slept in the house.

Then we went to stay with my stepfather's family, in Loir-et-Cher. The whole family was really nice. And since I was quiet, everything went fine.

I began to forget about my bathroom for a while. I didn't say anything most of the time. I didn't attract attention. I was a bit on my guard, but I made the most of the freedom.

Another important summer was the one when I spent two months with my grandmother. I was older then, about nine. They must have been at a loss where to put me again. They went off on holiday on their own. So I landed up at my grandmother's, in the country.

I remember the first day I arrived: I was completely lost. In a dream. Floating on air. Standing next to the car, I thought I was still locked in my hole. I didn't understand, I didn't move an inch because I was sure I was about to wake up from the dream... My brother came to fetch me.

It was a real farm with hens, rabbits, dogs, cats and a goat. We took the goat into the field and collected eggs. We tended the garden, which I remember being very big.

# THE BOY BEHIND THE DOOR

I was discovering the world, it was paradise.

My grandmother took me riding on her Solex. I felt really good with her. In the mornings, I would wake up to a ray of sunlight on my bed and the cock crowing.

I told her I wanted to stay with her for ever and go to school in the nearby village.

I hoped with all my might that they wouldn't come back for me and I could stay there. Sometimes I had a strong desire to tell her everything but I was scared she wouldn't believe me or would think I was mad.

So I lied to her about my hands.

Just like my parents lied to her about me, about school, about my life . . .

After this brief spell of paradise the summer ended and they came to get me. But I had developed a taste for freedom and enough strength to seek it later.

After my return from the paradise of my grandmother, my mother put me in her bedroom, tied to the bed.

It was one year after this, during the summer, that I tried to escape.

I don't know where I found the strength to do it. But I was propelled outside by some phenomenal force.

I was tied by a green leather dog's lead to a chain, which was fastened by a padlock and hung from the bed. The bedroom window was open and my mother was out shopping.

I found a knife in the bedside table. I cut through the leather lead. I think I took some sheets and hung them from the balustrade of the window.

I heard the key turn in the front door. I

lowered myself to the second floor – we lived on the third. I jumped down onto the garage roof, I broke some tiles, my right leg went right through, I fell off the roof, I split my skull open and sprained my ankle. I ran off limping, with blood everywhere.

A man walking his dog spotted me and called out to a couple who were walking by. The three of them took me to the police station at Neuilly-sur-Marne.

There they asked me my name, where I lived. I didn't know anything. At least, I didn't say anything. So they took me to the hospital.

I don't know how my mother found out. But she came that evening and brought me some toy soldiers.

I stayed in hospital for a month. The whole of August 1980. The weather was fine. I wanted to go to the seaside. My room had a balcony and a television, and there was a games room in the hospital. It was a real paradise.

I remember I would go into the nurses' office and telephone home. My mother would answer, I would hear her voice and hang up. It was always her who answered, never my stepfather. Sometimes she was angry. I don't know why I did it: to see if she was there? To hear her voice? As if, momentarily, I had a certain power . . .?

Maybe she wanted to leave me there for good?

At the hospital, after a while, they asked me when my parents would be coming to get me. I wasn't in any hurry. I haven't told the story very well. It has all become a bit vague. .

But at the end of August, they came to take me back and I returned to my prison.

I have always thought that I was born with misfortune. I had it at my back. Like a shadow. I anticipated it. I wasn't at peace. I was on the wrong track. Like an animal who can sense danger. Without being able to see it or know what it is.

Even when I was with the old foster mother I knew I didn't belong there and something was going to happen.

I sometimes still have the feeling that disaster is running after me, that I am being caught up by evil, but also the sense that I will manage to escape it at the last minute.

There was plenty of suffering for everyone. My mother's lawyer said to me one day, 'Your mother has suffered a lot.' He was the second person to say that to me.

And my grandmother? Her life can't have been all that great. So I searched into their two lives . . .

My grandmother is nearly seventy-six. She's an old lady, and she's seen it all. It wasn't easy for her to pass judgement on what has happened. She has white hair, cut short. Now I'm taller than her. She resembles both me and my mother. She always wore an overall when she was working. She loved me, I think. I always trusted her. She is the person I like best in this family.

The testimonies during the trial which retraced her life said lots of bad things. But I'm sure that she didn't have an easy life. It was a lonely life. She must have found it hard bringing up her children.

Now she has lost a daughter and gained a grandson. Her daughter she had already lost when my mother went off to live her life in Paris at the age of fourteen. They didn't get on at all.

In place of a mother who never was one I

have gained a grandmother 'mother', because she feels more like a mother than a grandmother. Even if I don't see her, I know that she exists.

Three years ago, we had a big argument. I can't remember what it was all about. I had gone to spend a few days with her during the holidays. At one point, she said, 'But you're nothing but a bastard!'

It was like being stabbed with a knife. It was a horrible thing to say. I tried to reply. But I bottled it all up, as usual. I didn't say anything.

I kept my anger inside, underground.

I resented her deeply. The only member of my family to say she loved me, and she said that to me . . .! I felt rejected. Sad. Very unhappy . . . I haven't been back to see her since.

Time has helped me to understand, and so, perhaps, has this story I am putting together bit by bit. I get the feeling she was addressing someone other than me. Her daughter, for example.

What she could no longer say to her she said to me. She also considered my mother as a bastard. Her history with her daughter was the same as that of my mother with me: we were both fatherless. My grandmother must have resented my mother. She found it hard to love her. And my mother repeated the same situation in making me a bastard. So she can't pass judgement on her.

They are both equally stubborn. Despite being completely different: my grandmother is a peasant. My mother is lower middle-class, fanatical about cleanliness – she didn't like walking through mud. But they are both heads of their families. And I'm pig in the middle! Between the pair of them. One on each side. That's the feeling I have now.

My grandmother and I now need to sort out our differences so we can talk together again in peace.

I don't think I'm angry any more.

We moved to Brétigny in July 1981. The year following my escape attempt.

They must have felt uneasy about staying in Neuilly-sur-Marne. Besides, she had given my brother's name at the hospital. I was receiving treatment under a false name!

Anyway, as I discovered later, they had found new jobs in the south of the city: he was manager of a small supermarket, and she was chief cashier, something like that. In other words, they were going up in the world.

I didn't really understand what the preparations were all about. There was lots of toing and froing in the house. The move took place very quickly.

They had rented a van. She bundled me out of the house, very quickly, like a thief, and put me in the back of the car, underneath some blankets. My brother sat on her knee, my stepfather drove. I had just turned eleven, my brother was ten.

The flat in Brétigny was a lot bigger. You entered directly into a wide corridor. The kitchen, opposite the door, was large and bright. Further down the corridor, the living room was on the right, with a double window. Then the bathroom, on the left, and immediately afterwards my parents' bedroom. Opposite, my brother's room. And, between the two rooms, at the end of the flat and the corridor, my cupboard.

She made me go inside, as soon as we arrived. Without a word. Without a moment to draw breath.

The cupboard measured 2 metres by 1.7 metres. I read that on the specification later. With two shelves on one side.

They unpacked their stuff and settled in.

She brought me a bucket – no question of me using the toilet next to the bathroom in the corridor; it was too far – and a foam mattress, which she put on the shelf. Then she double-locked the cupboard door. I was locked up once more.

There, a new order of suffering began. I was no longer beaten, but simply forgotten, totally abandoned. Thinking about it now, it might even have been better to be beaten than left alone in silence in the dark. I could no longer see anything. Not a glimmer of light got through the door. Total darkness.

In the beginning, she brought me a bowl quite regularly. By that I mean every morning and evening. Then gradually this became erratic, sometimes skipping whole days.

She forgot about me in my cell. I didn't exist any more. I was erased. Finished. I could go days without anything to eat or drink. I tried to keep calm, not to get too upset. I could feel it all boiling up inside. So I stretched out and lay alone in the dark without moving. Without crying out. To save my strength.

I didn't want her to see my weakness, my fear. Everything went on in my head, in silence.

I didn't want to ask her for anything. When she brought me food I wanted to refuse it but my courage failed me. I was hungry. I felt dizzy when I stood up. Burning hot, I was half dead.

These hunger strikes could last as long as four days. Each time, I thought I was going to die. Then she would turn up with a bowl of soup or something else, quite unidentifiable, or sometimes a bowl of coffee, which she placed on the floor. I no longer remember what this food tasted like. And in spite of myself I threw myself on it and wolfed it down.

I now believe she could have finished me off there in Brétigny.

Once, they went off for a week.

I guessed that it would be longer than usual. In the dark I touched what she had left me to eat, there was more than usual: cheese, fruit, a bottle of water, bread and some other stuff. In any case, nothing to choke on! One week, totally alone, in the dark, it's a long time. Terribly long. I organised my food the best I could, by touch.

What bothered me as well was the stink. My pail was beginning to smell bad. What's more, I had absolutely no idea how long I would be left on my own. I can say a week now, after the event.

In the course of time, life became 'organised'. At night, I stretched out on the foam mattress. There was enough room. Every now and then, she took me into the bathroom to give me a wash. I learned to orientate myself by sounds, by touch and by smell. Even now I can live in the dark easily, like a blind person. I need glasses just for reading or watching a film.

I heard everything. I knew everything that went on in the flat. I was constantly on the lookout. I knew my mother's step when she came in. I knew where she hid the key to the cupboard door simply by the sound it made when she dropped it into the pot on the bathroom shelf.

This sometimes came in handy on Wednesdays. My brother didn't go to school and he was often at home on Wednesday afternoons. My mother was at work. So my brother opened my door. We would go to the kitchen and have something to eat. We even put the television on. We didn't talk much. Silence reigned, even with him.

# THE BOY BEHIND THE DOOR

When the time came for my mother to return home I went back into my cupboard. It was these little windows to the outside world, where it was possible to live, that helped me get through the rest without dying.

When my brother couldn't find the key straight away I gave him instructions through the door, since I had heard my mother put it in one place or another. Because she changed the place according to her mood. But when the key really couldn't be found anywhere he would slide some little books under the door. I managed to read, or rather, make out the pictures by the faint glimmer of light that reached the cupboard during the daytime.

On one of these Wednesdays, we were eating in the kitchen. Suddenly we heard the front door open. In a panic I darted into the wardrobe where my stepfather kept his things, the one in my brother's room, at the opposite end of the corridor from the kitchen. I could have gone straight back into my cupboard. But I didn't. I don't know why I chose the wardrobe. So, I ended up bent double under the coats. My heart was beating twenty to the dozen. I thought everyone would hear it. And then my stepfather came to get something from the wardrobe. I heard him come and look. He went away then came back again. I was as motionless as a statue. Finally he closed the wardrobe door and breathed a huge sigh. Then I heard the front door slam. I didn't even hear what he said to my brother. He must have seen me. He must surely have opened the wardrobe door deliberately. He had heard me hiding myself there. My brother was in a tight corner too.

That evening, my stepfather didn't say anything to my mother. She probably would have killed me. We carried on with these Wednesday afternoons, only less frequently and with a bit more caution.

I thought about death. I had no real image of it, I just thought about it as a disappearance. One evening, my mother came to my cupboard to tell me that the husband of the lady upstairs had just died. 'Behave yourself, don't make a racket, there's a man lying dead upstairs.' This made quite an impression on me. This death was on my mind all night.

What if that happened to me too? What if I died here, all alone, without anyone knowing, in my cupboard? I had moments of extreme anxiety, without knowing exactly what was happening to me.

I had another fear: fire or a gas leak. At Neuilly, during the time I was under the bed in the bedroom, the firemen came. They must have broken down the doors to put out a fire. There was a lot of noise and an unusual amount of rushing about in the building. And I was tied to the bed and didn't know what was going on. If only the flat weren't deserted. Everyone had gone down into the street, including my mother. She had left me there.

It was a gas leak in the neighbouring flat. When I realised what had happened I was very scared, like a delayed reaction.

So at Brétigny I was on my guard. I was constantly sniffing the air, especially when I was alone in the flat.

I was obsessed by the thought of some disaster like that.

One day, my mother left a pan on the stove, all day. I was terrified. The burning smell reached my nostrils. I couldn't do a thing. And of course this was a day when there would be no one home until evening. I can remember my stepfather getting angry when he came home. I heard the pair of them shouting at each other. I didn't feel safe, and I continued sniffing the air from inside my hole.

The days were the same as the nights. Days went past, looking through the lock at the small amount of light that came through it, watching the daylight go . . . waiting for them to come home, listening out for new sounds . . .

I knew more or less the time my brother came home from school. But often he brought some friends home to play with and ignored me completely. I could hear them chattering and having fun in the bedroom next to me. In the end, my brother and I only saw each other on Wednesdays.

My stepfather sometimes came home for lunch. He turned on the radio in the kitchen. I always hoped that he would open the doors, at least the kitchen door. And that I might take advantage of him being there to get some more light. But he would shut himself in the kitchen on his own. He would have his food, then switch off the radio and go. Everything closed in again on the silence. My darkness was even darker.

At moments like that I felt an infinite sadness.

I spent one year in the dark. I wouldn't have been able to carry on much longer like that. The time I spent in the cupboard was much harder and more terrible than the time in the bathroom or the bedroom.

It was uninterrupted night. A night without end. With the feeling of having been forgotten, abandoned by the whole world. The dark is death.

I thought a great deal in the dark. Perhaps to avoid dying . . . Luckily I had images of my grandmother's farm which I ran like a film, dreaming that I might return there one day. And images of the sea, still . . . But I knew nothing about the world. I was like an animal.

Even now, night-time takes me back to that cupboard and the disgusting images return . . . I can't sleep without the light on. Otherwise the old thoughts come back . . . I see terrible visions . . .

Light gives me security. It gives me the time to organise my thoughts. I can listen to music or read. It's soothing. I only need a little light when I go to sleep. But in the dark the fear comes back. And the anguish with it. Especially when I am alone.

Even if I had no idea about the outside world, I dreamed a lot.

I imagined myself going to school, learning to read and write. Everything seemed easy outside this cupboard. Life must be wonderful outside!

As they often listened to the radio, always the same station, I let myself be lulled by the music which reached my ears.

That night lasted one year. The atmosphere in the flat became more and more heated. I heard them shouting constantly. Things were obviously bad between them.

One evening, my mother invited round some friends. I don't recall if my stepfather was there as well. The fact is that they sat up talking till late, and one of her friends stayed the night. The next morning they left in a hurry to go to work. My mother came back up; she must have brought me something in my cupboard but, in all the turmoil, she forgot to lock my door.

She left. I was all alone with my door open. For all I know, in the end she may have done it deliberately.

# THE BOY BEHIND THE DOOR

I had long hoped that she might one day forget to lock the door. Yet, when it happened, I hesitated.

I couldn't bring myself to go. I didn't dare. I can't explain this very well. I said to myself: 'I won't do anything wrong, she'll see that I stayed put, maybe she'll forget again tomorrow.'

I was afraid: afraid to leave, afraid of the outside, afraid to stay, afraid of what she might still do to me. I didn't know where I was at or what I should do. I was paralysed. The dog was lying on the bed. She was looking at me. She was trembling. As if she suspected something . . . I will never forget that look. I was sad to leave her. She had been my only friendly companion during all those years.

I wandered round the flat. I went from the corridor to the bedrooms. I came back to the kitchen. I ate a little. I couldn't make a decision. I felt really sick, and very nervous.

Then all of a sudden, it came: I opened my brother's wardrobe, took an anorak, a cap and a pair of tennis shoes that were too big for me.

I gathered together all the loose change that was lying about in the bedrooms and the living room. It wasn't going to weigh me down much.

I opened the door. I was outside.

When I got downstairs, I realised I had forgotten the purse. I dashed back upstairs. The dog was still on the bed, motionless. I picked up the money and ran back downstairs.

Opposite our block, on the pavement, people were looking at me. I was rigid with fear. It was hot. It was August. But I didn't know that.

I had never been outside on my own. I was in the street with the intention of going to my grandmother's. I had no idea where she lived. In fact, she lived a good two hundred kilometres away. I don't think I would ever have made it. It was impossible. I had no idea what direction to take, I didn't know the name of her village, nothing.

I walked aimlessly. Mechanically. Without thinking. I turned round every time a car stopped at a red light, thinking it might be my mother or my stepfather. I was getting more and more afraid.

To get off the street and find a place to hide, I went into a garden. The gate was open. I wandered round the garden a bit. Then I curled up in a ball under some shrubs. Some people came out of the house. There were quite a few of them. They must have been a large family, or else it was a social gathering.

They were talking as they came towards me. I couldn't hear very well. I was curled up like a hedgehog. They said: 'Is he dead? What's going on?'

So I leaped to my feet and started talking very quickly. I told them everything in one go: the cupboard, my burnt hands . . . I begged them: 'Don't send me back home . . .'

After that, everything happened quickly. They put me in the dining room. They called the police. I was sitting between two ladies. I can't remember what I said.

The police came and took me away. They wanted to know where I lived. They were very suspicious. They phoned the station to check I wasn't a runaway.

I didn't know the name of my street. I probably could have recognised the place. But deep down I was sure of one thing at least: it was better to play the idiot with the police than to have to face my mother. She'd have managed to convince the police that she was looking for me or God knows what. I would have ended up back there again.

I was thinking about all that in the car as we drove around the town and I repeated like a parrot: 'No, that's not it.'

I spent the evening at the station.

I answered their questions in as much detail as possible. I didn't stop talking. I described things, explained them. Like a robot. The words came out easily.

It must be quite obvious that I had lived in a cupboard. That's all I had in my head.

They must have thought I was mad at times.

I think they forgot to give me anything to eat.

After a medical check-up, around one o'clock in the morning, I ended up in a home in Brétigny. They gave me a bed for the night. I remember when I got up in the morning I put on my cap and someone said: 'Have you got lice or what?' I let that insult pass, but it wasn't a good start!

They clothed me and fed me. People brought me presents: a watch, a remote-control four-wheel-drive amphibian! I'd never seen anything like it! There were other things as well which I can't remember.

That's where the journalists got in to see me. But when they asked me questions I had already switched off. I was drifting in a semi-conscious state. I was no longer there. Reeling. I had no image in my mind. It was like I was anaesthetised. But I was alive. Able to breathe the air of freedom.

They brought the little dog for me. I had her with me, in the home, but some of the kids were violent, and I was worried about her. Later, with a counsellor, I would take her to my stepfather's mother. She would be safer there.

When I escaped, my brother was on holiday. It must have been a shock to him to learn that his parents had been arrested. They put him straight into a social services home.

Life can't have been too simple for him

either. He wasn't allowed to talk about me outside the house. I didn't exist outside the bathroom, the bedroom or the cupboard. At school he was an only child. At home he was witness to things he could talk about even less. It must have seemed strange to him and not very easy to live with.

He was a year and a half younger than me. I don't know what I meant to him. He did all he could to help me. Obviously I don't bear a grudge against him. He isn't involved in all this.

My mother treated him like a king. He could have anything he wanted. If he had a cold, she called the doctor. He had all the toys in the world . . . This difference in the way my brother and I were treated has left very painful scars.

Physically, he is quite tall. Taller than me, at least. He is pretty solidly built. He has blue eyes, and curly, almost blond hair. He has a nice face. He's a good-looking lad. He is more sporty than intellectual; but definitely intelligent.

We never used to talk much, but when they

put us in separate homes, we visited one another at weekends. We did things together and ended up getting on quite well. When they got out of prison he went to live with his father. He was able to continue his studies.

Some weekends he came with me to see my mother. I felt that he was happy that things were like that, that it gave him pleasure. We were learning how to live together from scratch.

Even if we have never discussed the past I feel now that I have done everything necessary for us to find each other again, to open up new possibilities.

I'd love for us all to live together again, him, my mother and me, like a real family . . . But, we've lost touch. We don't talk to each other any more. I don't know anything about him these days.

As for seeing him again, why not? But that can only come from him now. He knows where to find me. He has enough sense to know that I trust him.

After my escape I ended up in a social services home where I stayed for a while. I didn't have a clue about anything. At first I must have imagined that all men were like my stepfather and all women like my mother. I had no experience of things at all. You could call it naivety. It was like I was a kind of animal. I was mentally retarded.

Words, in themselves, weren't all that important to me. Just the absolute minimum required. I thought that you just had to learn to read and write and then you could do anything!

I mean any job . . .! I had dreams like that, of becoming an airline pilot or a train driver . . . I was soon put straight on that!

Right at the start of my life in freedom I

went to the school in the home. I learned to read and do sums. That was OK. Even if it was hard to keep up with the pace.

I was in with children who were younger than me. I remember at meal-times I had a voracious appetite. I always cleared my plate. I think I was a bit over the top.

A few months later they put me in a Ministry of Justice home at Evry. I was twelve. Evry was like a small family. There weren't many of us. I was a bit wild. I made a lot of noise. I talked a lot. It wasn't that the others frightened me, I just wasn't used to it.

The teachers taught me how to live. I continued to go to school. I learned about life: talking, playing, eating, fighting. The lot! Everything was important.

I was pampered by the teachers. They were all really good with me. Things couldn't have been better. I had found everything that I needed. I was very lucky.

I learned everything all at once. Discovered everything. I went to winter-sports school, summer camp, to the seaside. I remember the first time I saw the sea again! The sand, the beach, the blue sky, the waves – it was marvellous! Paradise . . .!

I learned to ski and to ride a horse. I've even got a diving diploma! I discovered lots of things in a very short amount of time. The teachers supervised me well. I have nothing but good memories of those years.

The biggest problem was school itself. I didn't know how to make the most of the opportunities my studies offered me. I was a bit overwhelmed by it.

Afterwards I felt guilty about it. It was a disaster. I never did any work. I stopped learning things. I didn't make the grade.

Now I really regret it. I wanted to learn, to know, to read, to pick up enough things to help me find a suitable job. I don't really know what. Designing clothes, fashion, that interests me. But I don't know how to go about it.

Alongside my life in the home, I went to see T.L., a psychiatrist.

The first time I went to his office I felt immediately at ease. I trusted him from the start. Even though I was pretty violent at that time. Ridiculously aggressive! It was as if I could get angry, fly into a rage – and it really was rage at that point – for no reason whatever. He was sitting behind his desk. He was waiting. I knew he was listening to me. That he would help me bring light to my story.

First he said to me: 'Tell me about your mother.' So I set off at top speed . . .!

I went to see him several times a week.

Then we made things with modelling clay, did drawings. We played. We chatted. He wrote down stories which I told him. He probably still has them stashed away somewhere.

It was good. He did me a lot of good. I believe he helped me to get free of my hatred. To placate it. This allowed me to go to see my mother in prison without any ulterior motives. He suggested I should see her. He must have felt I was up to it.

I went to see my mother in prison, once, at Fleury-Mérogis. I must have been thirteen. Almost a year after my escape and her arrest. Afterwards, we met in the judge's office.

I was prepared, if you like. Ready to see her.

My brother went along as well.

In fact, I wanted to see her.

T.L. had helped me a lot with this meeting.

I was curious about what I might find. About who I would meet.

I was going to look at her, to see her differently.

I had a strange mixture of feelings: both curiosity, without fear or apprehension particularly, and bewilderment.

As if I didn't know this particular mother. As if I was going to encounter someone different. The situation was the reverse of the one I had always experienced: she was locked up and I was free.

I looked forward to seeing what effect that would produce.

I arrived at the judge's office. My mother kissed me. Then the judge left us alone for a short while.

It was only then, on this first visit, that I found out for sure that my stepfather wasn't my father. I didn't have his name, but my mother's. So I had a father somewhere. Who had nothing to do with this man, my mother's companion, father of my brother, to whom I was nothing. My thoughts were all confused. A jumble of memories came back: the photo

# THE BOY BEHIND THE DOOR

I found in the bedside table of that man who resembled me (unless I dreamed it), my mother's comment when we were watching television: 'There's Daddy singing.' This became an obsession with me and I badgered my mother about this unknown father.

She wouldn't say anything. Not who he was, what he was called. Just that he abandoned her when she was pregnant and had only six hundred francs to her name.

Knowing that he left her a total of six hundred francs didn't get me much further forward. She really clammed up on this question. And I wanted so much to know! My hunger wasn't satisfied.

I asked her questions about herself as well. About the reasons for what had happened.

Then the judge came back. We sat there together for a while, then I left.

I went to see her a good few times before the trial. I can't remember how many times. Her and my stepfather as well. Separately. Except for one time when we all saw each other together, with my brother there too.

Gradually, we learned to talk without an intermediary. It was a real learning process for us as a family. For their part, they were learning how to be parents. She, how to be a mother, perhaps. I was having to learn not to see them in a bad light. To get the hatred out of my system. I told myself that there was something to be done there and then at this point in our lives. That it was possible to live together again. That it was possible to imagine having a life like other people's. I was going to rediscover some parents. I needed a family, roots. So we could at least try, attempt to create a real family. Like I had never had. Which would have been a point of support in my existence. I thought all these things. I really wanted it to be possible. And our meetings went well.

I spoke freely. Everything was normal. I was happy. I remember I told them about school, what was happening at the home, the stamp collection I had started.

There is always some way to connect again. One or two years were enough to placate and relieve my hatred. In its place I had found forgiveness, without realising it. What was left was the connection, the ties.

# THE BOY BEHIND THE DOOR

*

Then there was the trial, which terrified me.

I said at the start of the book that I didn't say anything in court because my brother had asked me not to.

But now that I have reached this point in my story I can say that my feelings at that time were divided: that it was not only my brother's request, but also everything that had happened with my mother during the visits at the judge's office.

It was difficult to be clear, to define my desire, which was both that life should go on normally, but also to tell of the harm that had been done to me . . .

The desire that this whole horror should stop and that we might all escape from it was the strongest. I continued seeing my mother and I wrote to the Minister of Justice.

Dear sir,

My parents are in prison in Versailles and Fleury because of the way they treated me when I was a child. I was locked in a cupboard. I have relived my story, and the things I have learned about what happened to me are what is making me write to you today. I told my ideas to Doctor Lainé, who helped me very much and whom I trust completely.

I need to rediscover my mother and my stepfather in freedom . . . I will be seventeen on 29 May. I need them to get out as quickly as possible . . .

*Extract from the letter to the Minister of Justice.*

I went to a holiday camp with the home and the school. It was a new experience for me. There were lots of us on the first trip. A real crowd.

The first morning, there were so many people in the breakfast room that I was seized by panic. I didn't dare enter. Luckily, a girl from the home was there with me and she helped me overcome my fear and go in to eat my breakfast.

Little by little I got used to it.

I adapted.

Then there were other camps where everything was fine.

I started noticing girls.

My only experience of women had been my mother. But the girls I saw here were nothing like her. They didn't frighten me. They were completely different.

During one of these trips I spotted a very beautiful girl. All the boys were looking at her. I told myself that she wasn't for me. But in fact we ended up spending an evening together. I was so happy. Except, the next day, I behaved badly.

As usual I turned up late for breakfast. A bit out of breath. My head was muddled. Everyone was looking at me. Including her. I didn't say a word, not even a good morning, to anyone. I didn't speak to her. I thought I would go and see her later. But it was too late. She got cross, or something. She resented it. Anyway, she made me pay. And I lost her.

There was one who was fourteen years old, but who looked a lot older. She was hard-working. She had a mother and a little sister. I think I babbled like an idiot and she kept me hanging on for ages!

She had never gone out with a boy – at least, that's what she said – but she was very pretty, so I tried to change that. She kept saying that she would give me an answer at the end of the week. Good of her!

# THE BOY BEHIND THE DOOR

I waited patiently.

In the end we got together almost every evening . . .! It was the holidays . . .

Basically, you're always having to fight a battle with girls. You either win or you lose. Yet it's stupid to talk about winning or losing. That's not what it's about. So long as you like each other and get on well . . .

I prefer quiet people. I like girls who have lots of energy and confidence, but who don't go around yelling. Who don't get worked up. I don't yell. I don't get worked up. I don't have a great deal of experience yet, but my impression is that yelling achieves nothing . . .

I know I look young for my age. I don't know if that's good or bad. Maybe it meant that, at fourteen, I didn't come across as an old fool . . .!

One time, I had problems because of my hands.

It was on a class trip to Saint-Aignan, in Nièvre. I told this girl that I wanted to go out with her. She wouldn't give me an answer straight away. Not only was it not a very nice situation, but she got together with her friends in a room to talk about it. I felt like I was caught in a trap, judged, a bit betrayed. I listened through the door. One of the boys asked her if it was because of my hands that she didn't want to go out with me.

I felt really bad. I wanted to drop it. I also felt a bit angry. Later, I was able to ask her if the real reason was my hands. She said no, she had another boyfriend in Paris and she just wasn't interested.

It disgusted me and depressed me: I could be refused because of my hands. I could be rejected. My hands excluded me from things. They were a handicap that went with me everywhere.

At the start of my life in the home I was given thorough check-ups by the doctors. One thing they did was take me to the Boucicaut hospital for an operation on the skin which had formed between my thumb and index finger. The finger bones of my right hand were retracted. I couldn't stretch out my fingers. So they gave me an elasticated device to use for a few months to help me correct this. The doctor who looked after me was a hand specialist and he was very good.

Today I can extend my fingers almost normally. I could play a stringed instrument, a bass or a guitar, for example. Playing the piano would be more difficult. I still get a pain in my index and middle fingers.

I remember, one day at this hospital, I was

watching a programme on Mesrine* with a nurse. She told me that Mesrine's wife had had an operation in this very hospital and had slept in the bed I was using now. I felt really strange all of a sudden . . . They should sell this bed, they'd get a good price!

It's true that everyone took good care of me. But that didn't stop me being as badly behaved as the others.

On a trip to Mont-Saint Michel with some people from Ivry, some of my group thought it might be interesting to go shop-lifting. I went along with them; I did my share. Once, we got caught. I was cocky, I played the fool and laughed like an idiot. As if I found the whole thing amusing!

A policeman asked me if I was completely retarded. 'Yes, probably,' I replied. Then they let us go.

The problem was that we carried on. We stole little gold chains. Whatever we could get our hands on, really. It was fatal! Of course we got caught again. We had to take everything

* An infamous French gangster.

back to the shop. The monitors who were looking after us got a real ticking off from the police.

We were all down at the station, stripped to our underpants and searched. I could have died of shame. I had never done anything like that before.

One of the boys, who was obviously trying to make out he was harder than the others, asked casually, 'If we made a run for it, what would you do?' 'We'd make life hard for you.' Thanks a lot!

There was a pack of Gauloises on a shelf, behind the policemen. I really felt like taking it. I was so cross. I just wanted to do something to take my mind off my shame, some little game, some act of defiance: like pinching their cigarettes from under their noses.

There were quite a few North Africans in our group and one of the policemen couldn't resist asking them why they didn't stay in their own country. Congratulations. There was a bad atmosphere.

This wasn't a brilliant episode. But at least since then I haven't been tempted to steal anything at all, anywhere.

When I am alone – that is, when I don't have to talk to anyone – I can't stop myself thinking: I mean, I need to think before doing anything at all. This caused me a few problems when I was at school.

I was already constantly late because I was used to sleeping for hours in the morning: I never managed to wake up or get up in time. I didn't have the same way of life as other people. In a way, I lived like a savage.

When I got up I needed a quarter of an hour to think, during which I didn't do anything else. By then, I was already behind schedule.

After taking a shower, during breakfast, I stayed immersed in my thoughts, it was vital to me.

★

# THE BOY BEHIND THE DOOR

Everything took a huge amount of time. I had my head in the clouds. It was a nuisance when it came to day-to-day life.

People would often say to me, 'David, get a move on. What are you thinking about? What are you doing?'

I would always arrive late: at school and later on at my first jobs. I was treated like a waster. Yet I don't think of myself as lazy. But it is true that I need more time to myself than the average person. Time just for my thoughts: to assemble them before going into the everyday world.

Now I can manage to concentrate on my work if people leave me in peace. Without passing comment. But even then I have to make an effort to banish the thoughts which keep turning over in my head. This can be pretty tough. Sometimes I think about all the sadness of the world. At times like that I have real trouble sticking to what I'm doing. Naturally, my work is affected and I get told off. That's how it is.

I spent eight years in all at the home. I was thirteen when I went there and twenty when I left.

I was just approaching fifteen when the trial took place in 1985. So I had been living at the home for almost three years. I was still going to school, but to be honest I wasn't working very hard. At least, not hard enough to make up for lost time.

I was still seeing T.L. regularly. He came along to support me at the trial. He was a witness. And my mother got out of prison. End of 1986 or beginning of 1987, I can't remember.

I don't know whether my letter to the Minister of Justice speeded up her release or not, or whether she had done her time in any case. The fact is, she got out.

# THE BOY BEHIND THE DOOR

At first she lived in a room in a house for young girls at Charenton. She worked as a cleaner. We went there at weekends, my brother and me. We all slept in her room. Maybe it would be the start of a new life? We had got back in touch with each other. It was good.

She stayed there a few months. Then she was able to move into a flat, also in Charenton.

It was a light apartment, with a corridor opening onto her bedroom, a living room, a kitchen and a bathroom. When my brother and I came to visit, she would lend us her bedroom and sleep in the living room. She had a few simple bits of furniture.

We went out together, the three of us. We chatted. In short, life seemed to be getting back to normal. We were learning how to live together from scratch. There was no tension, at least not on my part. My brother was happy.

I brought along my stamp collection and left it with her. That way, I came back to it at weekends. Perhaps I thought I might move in there permanently one day.

I was very attached to my stamp collection. I had started it at the home and I had assembled quite a treasure trove.

# THE BOY BEHIND THE DOOR

My mother was still working as cleaner at the young girls home, while she was looking for a job in the restaurant or retail trade, I can't remember which. Anyway, she had always managed in the past, no doubt she would find something.

I was discovering a different person. Someone I hadn't known before. She behaved normally, she was like all the other mothers!

Things went well between us for a few months.

Except, I still had these questions in my head. One day I brought them out into the open.

I needed to talk to my mother. I wasn't at war with her any more, I wasn't aggressive; I just wanted to understand. I mentioned the past. I wanted her to explain. Why? Why me? I wanted her to tell me who my father was. I wanted her to answer so much, just this once.

She couldn't do it, couldn't talk about the past. It was too unbearable. As soon as I broached the subject, she closed up, right up. It was too hard for her. Yet, I couldn't remain silent.

So, one day, she replied with total silence. She was no longer there.

It was New Year's Eve, 1987.

At the time I was working in a restaurant. I was on my own in the home that evening. I wanted to phone her to wish her a happy New Year. I hadn't seen her for some time. So I gave her a ring at her place, as usual. Someone I didn't know answered the phone. A wrong number.

I checked with directory enquiries that I hadn't made a mistake. They gave me another number. Fine. I ring this number and some-one else answers and tells me there is no one of that name on this number.

I was beginning to feel confused, scared. The sort of fear that paralyses you. I was stun-ned. As if I had been hit on the head. I sat in the kitchen for ages without moving. Trying to find a way out of the fog. What was going on? Where was she? Gone without letting me know or leaving an address. She didn't even leave a small note. Nothing. Nothingness. A void. No one left.

I felt angry and sad at the same time.

Once the initial shock had passed I rang my stepfather. He had heard nothing. He didn't know anything either. As for my brother, he was just as shocked as I was. We avoided talking about it.

I had such a need to find an explanation for things, to find words to tell my story, but with him I was careful, so as not to hurt him.

I took my mother's sudden disappearance personally. As soon as I had started to talk to her she had turned tail and fled. At that moment I felt totally alone.

My mother had disappeared. Taking her secret with her.

I started thinking about this air of mystery which surrounded her. I wanted to know about her past. It's difficult reconstructing the history of someone who isn't there.

My grandmother actually once said about her daughter that she gave the impression that she had no history. A smooth surface. My mother always needed a mask, a false appearance. But neither my grandmother nor I could get behind her performance.

The other people in the building liked her, and said that she adored children.

Now I am struggling with these contradictions and with her absence.

# THE BOY BEHIND THE DOOR

I'm not inside her head. I can't pass judgement. I can merely ask questions.

Does she bear a grudge against me?

Has she erased me from her life for good, or not? Do I have to disappear so that she can live? Or the other way round: does she have to disappear so that I can live?

Perhaps she wants to go away for ever.

I would love to know what has happened to her. I can see that she is still in my mind, that I can't separate myself from her. If she would only give me some sign of life, I would go to see her. I am no longer a hard person.

My mother is a very beautiful woman. And very mature. It's obvious that she has seen a lot of life. She is slim and not very tall. She is about forty-five, and looks young for her age.

She has a pretty face, and dyed blond hair. Her hair is naturally dark. She always has her hair done nicely, she is well-groomed. She makes herself up very well with dark eye shadow.

Her outward appearance is smooth, virtually flawless. Perhaps she has aged a bit now.

*

# THE BOY BEHIND THE DOOR

She has had a difficult life from the start.

When she was small she had to put up with a violent, alcoholic father. They were a large family, and they all had a miserable life. She said that her mother didn't love her, that she felt like she was excluded. My grandmother maintains the opposite, of course. She must have left home at a very young age. She learned how to manage on her own very quickly.

She is very bright.

She was young when she had me. Alone. Without a husband. And me without a father. I'm sure she didn't want a child at that time. It must have been very hard for her. She made me pay for her misfortune. We always make others pay for our misfortune, don't we?

Am I looking for excuses or trying to understand?

It is as if she had denied her identity, in a way. She wanted to wipe out her origins, which she was ashamed of. And yet she didn't know these, since she didn't know who her father was. When I came along I didn't fit into her scheme of things. She wanted to hide me. It must have been a terrible burden to her.

The brief fling and the split with my father, her new life with my stepfather and the birth of my brother, all these events didn't really leave any space for me. And then the fact that I didn't take to her very well, that there was nothing between us, didn't help matters.

Someone once said to me that my mother loved me in her way. I found that hard to believe. It was more like hate.

The reality I had lived with for eight years had nothing to do with love. They sometimes say that there's a thin dividing line between love and hate, but I can't see it!

The things she did to me were so serious, her reactions were so violent . . .

One thing has always bothered me: her tendency to deny all the evidence.

She was condemned for burning my hands. But she has never admitted to doing it. Her statements don't stand up: that I fell into the bidet while I was playing, that she put her laundry in to soak, that it was an accident, etc.

# THE BOY BEHIND THE DOOR

Even if I had fallen by accident, I would have got out very quickly and I wouldn't have been burned like that and only on my hands. She really has got everything wrong. It's obvious I was held down by force.

Later on, she maintained that she kept me locked up to hide my hands. Wrong. I was locked up a long time before I got burned.

She always refused to see a psychiatrist. As far as she was concerned, everything was fine. She never wanted to take responsibility for herself. I think that's a real shame.

Thinking about all this again, I tell myself that if we had lived together again, we would have remained in a state of mutual observation, unable to progress further with the weight of the past. I myself wasn't mature enough to confront her.

Now I can't see how we could get together again. And even if that happened, what possibilities are left? It's too late.

We would have been at a stand-off for the rest of our lives. You have to draw a line under those things which were never meant to be.

## THE BOY BEHIND THE DOOR

I wonder what will become of her when she is old enough to be a grandmother.

It is difficult to say whether she committed a crime of passion, a proper crime, or both.

I'm struggling with a ghost.

Life went on in the home, without her.

I left school.

I tried to find work, go out into the world to earn a living, as they say. I had no training. It was difficult to find work under those circumstances.

I didn't know much, except that I was in a real fix, and had to get out of it myself!

I got a youth training place in a restaurant in Ris-Orangis. On an eighteen-month contract. I learned quite a lot there. That job went well. Then I got a job in a warehouse in Montlhéry. I had to wrap up bicycle parts. It wasn't brilliant. But I didn't stay there very long.

I think I was drifting aimlessly at that time.

# THE BOY BEHIND THE DOOR

In life, in my head, in my search for what I might be able to do.

I got a job as a shop assistant at Corbeil. I left after six months. The atmosphere wasn't too good, to be honest it was awful, and the owner was weird.

I was nineteen and having trouble adapting to the reality of working life. Maybe my mother didn't kill me off when I was little, but the weight of the past is sometimes so heavy that it prevents me from doing things. I don't want to die, not at all. Even if at times everything is so difficult.

Difficult to find your place in life. Difficult to know what you really want to do. Difficult to be with other people, sometimes.

Around this time I began to lose touch with my brother. It was always me who rang him to find out his news. He never rang me. So I gave up. I didn't pick up the phone any more, and I heard no more about him.

I felt alone in the world.

A certain sadness returned. Along with bitterness and a type of anger at seeing all my plans and opportunities go to pieces. My mother had disappeared, my brother was leading his own life without bothering about mine. I was abandoned, forgotten. I had to get by on my own.

So, rather than keep this poisonous sadness inside me, I wanted to write it down. That's all there was left to do!

Could I have not written this and got over it some other way?

I think I would have remained stupid . . .!

The need to write down, to recount what happened to me is an old idea.

Writing is easier than speaking by itself.

I also wanted to bring it all out into the open, to stop this happening to others.

It was a good way to speak to lots of people at the same time, my family among them.

I had a need to clarify things, get my head in order, reconstruct my story.

I have been able to express my anger and sadness, and get the suffering out of my system. To push it far away in order to be rid of it.

But not in order to forget it.

In this way, I am alive!

# THE BOY BEHIND THE DOOR

I feel like I have set off on a search.
That I am on the way to new discoveries.
Gradually, instead of there being only questions, I am finding answers.

This book has been a sort of liberation. And an enriching experience.
I am not the same person now that I was at the start of this book.
It is all helping me to live.

Perhaps it is another sort of encounter. An encounter with the cowardice and shame of others. Those who have slunk off like thieves. A way of getting beyond all that.

Writing, speaking, is a way of finding the truth, my own truth. When you have too many questions inside you, you can't progress.
The moment comes when you have no choice but to express them.
I believe I have reached that moment.

# A Selected List of Non-Fiction Titles Available from Mandarin

While every effort is made to keep prices low, it is sometimes necessary to increase prices at short notice. Mandarin Paperbacks reserves the right to show new retail prices on covers which may differ from those previously advertised in the text or elsewhere.

The prices shown below were correct at the time of going to press.

All these books are available at your bookshop or newsagent, or can be ordered direct from the address below. Just tick the titles you want and fill in the form below.

Cash Sales Department, PO Box 5, Rushden, Northants NN10 6YX.
Fax: 0933 410321 : Phone 0933 410511.

Please send cheque, payable to 'Reed Book Services Ltd.', or postal order for purchase price quoted and allow the following for postage and packing:

£1.00 for the first book, 50p for the second; **FREE POSTAGE AND PACKING FOR THREE BOOKS OR MORE PER ORDER.**

NAME (Block letters) ................................................................................................................................

ADDRESS ................................................................................................................................................

................................................................................................................................................

☐ I enclose my remittance for .........................

☐ I wish to pay by Access/Visa Card Number

Expiry Date

Signature ................................................................................................................................................

Please quote our reference: MAND